Tiger Mask

Written by Alison Hawes

I want to be a tiger.

2

collage paste

tracing paper

3

I need an apron.

4

aprons

5

I need orange card.

black

orange

yellow

blue

white

I need scissors.

crayons

felt tips

scissors

REXEL

collage pasta

tracing paper

tissue paper

collage materials

white paper

card

coloured paper

modelling

9

I need black paint.

Grrr!